PILOT & HUXLEY

AND THE HOLIDAY PORTAL

Written and illustrated by

DAN McGUINESS

BOOK 2

A & C Black • London

FOR MY PARENTS ELAINE AND BILL McGUINESS. THANK YOU FOR SUPPORTING ME IN EVERYTHING I'VE DONE

First published in the UK in 2010 by
A & C Black Publishers Ltd
36 Soho Square, London, W1D 3QY

www.acblack.com

First published in Australia by
Omnibus Books
An imprint of Scholastic Australia Pty Limited

Text and illustrations copyright © 2010 Dan McGuiness
Design copyright © 2010 Dan McGuiness and Clare Oakes

The right of Dan McGuiness to be identified as the author and
illustrator of this work has been asserted by him in accordance
with the Copyrights, Designs and Patents Act 1988.

ISBN 978-1-4081-2860-2

A CIP catalogue for this book is available from the British Library.

This book is produced using paper that is made from wood
grown in managed, sustainable forests. It is natural, renewable and
recyclable. The logging and manufacturing processes conform
to the environmental regulations of the country of origin.

Printed and bound by C & C Offset, China

CHAPTER ONE:
THE VOID HOPPER

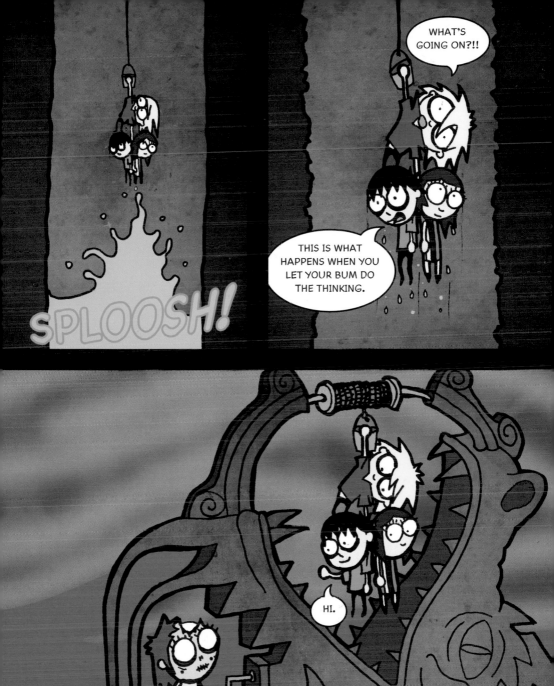

CHAPTER TWO:
DECK THE HALLS...

WELCOME, TRAVELLERS. BEFORE YOU PASS THROUGH MY PORTAL, YOU MUST ANSWER ONE QUESTION.

OINK!

HOLY HUXLEY! WHAT'S THAT HIDEOUS CREATURE?

MAYBE IT'S A RELATION OF YOURS.

WELL, MY COMRADES, THAT IS THE QUESTION YOU MUST ANSWER IF YOU WISH TO PASS. WHAT SORT OF ANIMAL IS THIS?

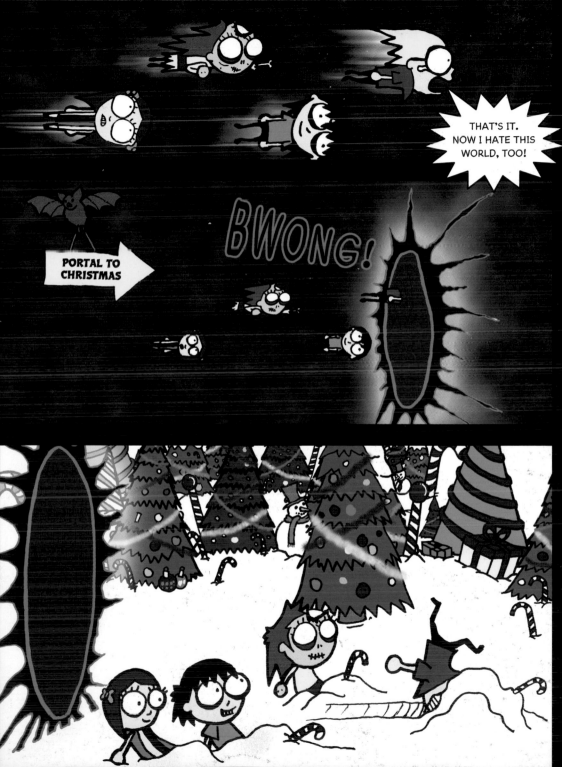

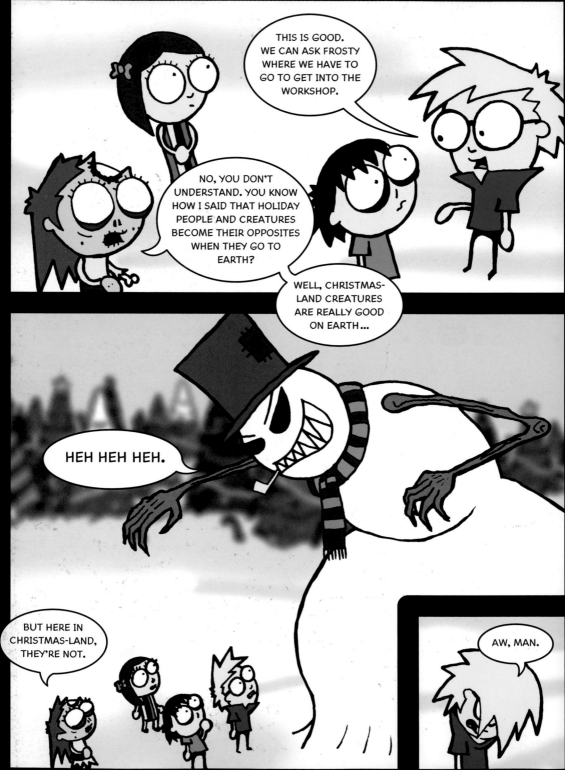

CHAPTER THREE:
THE EARTH-ENTERING CELEBRATION

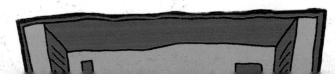

YEAH!

WOOHOO!

SO WITHOUT FURTHER ADO, I INTRODUCE THE MAN WHO MADE THIS ALL HAPPEN, SANTA CLAUS.

THANK YOU, THANK YOU!

ROAR!

CHEER!

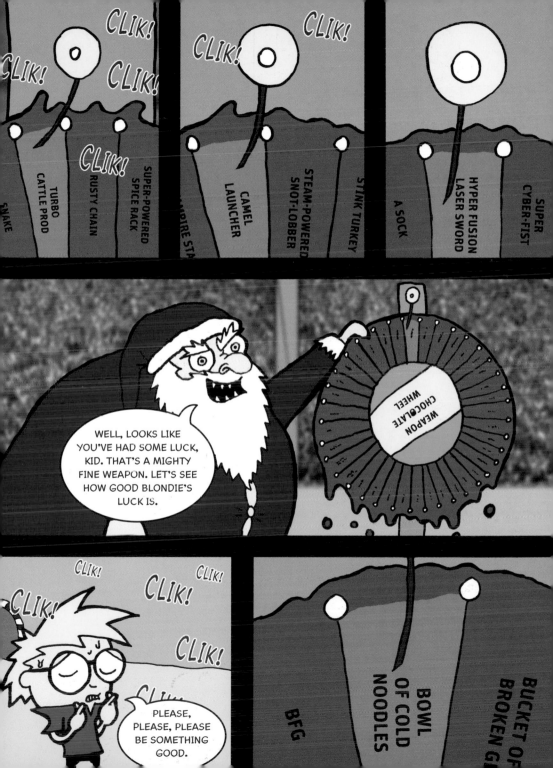

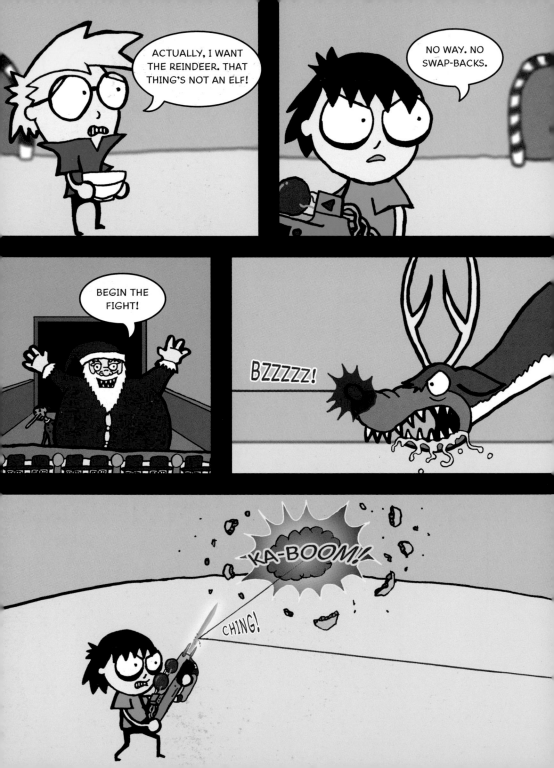

CHAPTER FOUR:
GOODBYE CHRISTMAS, HELLO TROUBLE

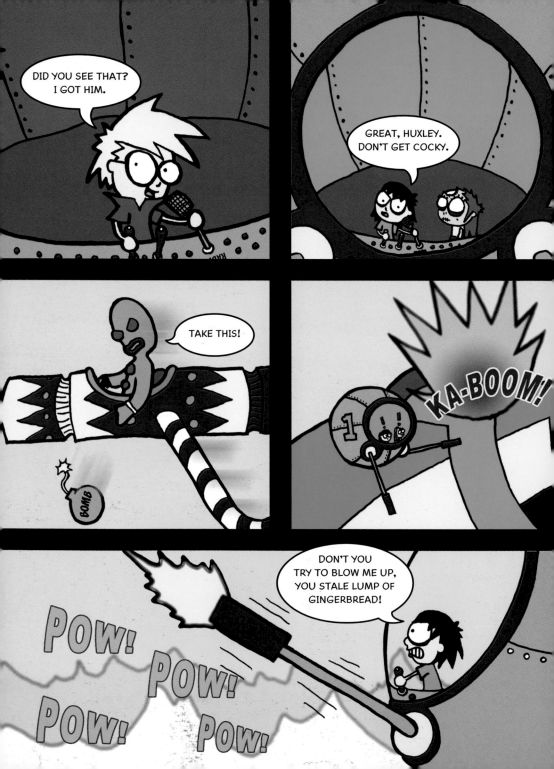

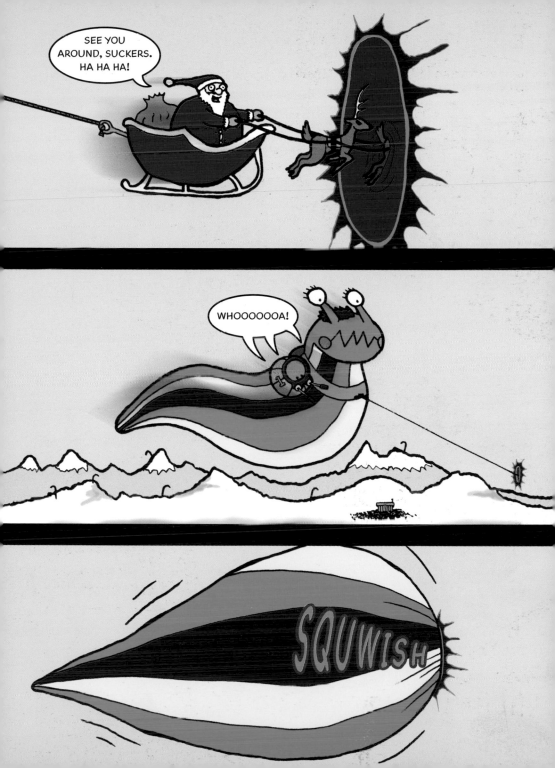

AFTERWORD

LOOK OUT FOR PILOT AND HUXLEY IN THEIR NEXT ADVENTURE!

DAN GREW UP UNDER CLOSE SCRUTINY IN A MILITARY FACILITY OF UNCERTAIN LOCATION.

THE MILITARY WAS TRYING TO HARNESS HIS AMAZING POWERS OF RADNESS. THEN ONE DAY AN EXPERIMENT WENT WRONG, GIVING DAN THE ABILITY TO COMMUNICATE TELEPATHICALLY WITH CATS.

UNBEKNOWN TO HIS CAPTORS, DAN FORMED A SECRET ARMY OF STRAY CATS.

DAN USED THE CAT ARMY TO BREAK OUT OF THE MILITARY FACILITY.

AFTER THEIR DRAMATIC ESCAPE, DAN AND THE CATS WENT INTO BUSINESS WRITING BOOKS. THE BOOK YOU'VE JUST READ IS ONE OF THESE.